USING PRIMARY SOURCES

Level B

with Document-Based Questions

GLOBE FEARON

Pearson Learning Group

CONTENTS

Model Lesson: Declaration of Independence

⭐ Here's the Skill ⬇

"We hold these truths to be self-evident, that all men are created equal. . . . "

The sentence above is familiar to almost all social studies students. It is from the Declaration of Independence—one of the most important historical documents in American history. A historical document is a written or printed paper that gives information about the past.

In this chapter, you will read historical documents that have helped shape our nation. Some are official government documents. Others are speeches that people have made. These documents record important events in our nation's history. They also help us understand how our government was formed and tell us what people were thinking and feeling in a specific time period.

Knowing how to gather information from a historical document can help you learn more about life in the past.

Here's Why ⌄

Being able to analyze historical documents will help you to learn how and why our country holds certain beliefs today. These beliefs include our laws and the policies of our government. Reading these documents will help you to understand what it means to be an American citizen.

Read *A Snapshot From History*. It will provide historical background for the historical document on page 6.

A Snapshot From History ▪▪▪▪▪▪▪▪▪▪▪▪▪▪▪

The first settlers in colonial America were ruled by the king of Great Britain. Yet by the late 1700s, many settlers believed that they should be free from Great Britain's rule. As tensions mounted in the colonies, war seemed to be the only way to break away from Britain. Angry colonists held **protests**, gave speeches, and wrote pamphlets demanding change.

A group of colonial leaders called on Thomas Jefferson to write a document declaring that the 13 colonies were no longer part of Great Britain. The document was called the Declaration of Independence. It explained why the colonies believed they should be free. It described the basic rights on which the United States was founded. It also explained that it is the government's job to protect these rights.

The Declaration of Independence was signed in Congress on July 4, 1776. It announced the creation of a separate nation—the United States of America.

Term To Know ≡

protest
  meeting held to express disapproval

# Here's How ⩣

Here is a step-by-step strategy to help you analyze historical documents that you may find on standardized tests. The following passage is from the Declaration of Independence.

From Declaration of Independence (1776)

- Identify the document.
- Identify when it was written.

When in the course of human events, it becomes necessary for one people to dissolve the political bands which have connected them with another, and to assume among the powers of the earth, the separate and equal station to which the laws of nature and of nature's God entitle them, a decent respect to the opinions of mankind requires that they should declare the causes which impel them to the separation.

- Identify the purposes of the document.

We hold these truths to be self-evident, that all men are created equal, that they are <u>endowed</u> [provided] by their Creator with certain <u>unalienable</u> [unable to be taken away] rights, that among these are life, liberty, and the pursuit of happiness. That to secure these rights, governments are instituted among men, deriving their just powers from the consent of the governed, that whenever any form of government becomes destructive of these ends, it is the right of the people to alter or to abolish it, and to institute new government, laying its foundation on such principles, and organizing its powers in such form, as to them shall seem most likely to effect their safety and happiness.

- Identify each part of the document.

- Find and look up any unfamiliar words.

Now, review the strategy on the next page to help you analyze this passage. Then, apply the strategy to the other historical documents in this chapter.

1. Read and Study

★ Identify the document. Determine when it was written.

★ Identify the parts of the document. Each part introduces a new idea.

★ Identify the purpose and audience of the document. Determine why and to whom the document was written.

★ Find and look up any unfamiliar words.

2. Ask Yourself Questions

Answer the following questions about the document on page 6.

1. When was this document written?

_____

2. Who wrote the document?

_____

3. What are the main ideas of the first paragraph?

_____

_____

4. What are the main ideas of the second paragraph?

_____

_____

_____

5. According to the document, why was it written?

_____

_____

3. Put It All Together

Tell how the document reflects what is going on during this period. Explain the colonists' point of view.

Analyzing Historical Documents

The Constitution of the United States

Here are two passages from the U.S. Constitution. Read *A Snapshot From History*. It will provide historical background for the document.

From The Constitution of the United States (1787)

We the people of the United States, in order to form a more perfect Union, establish justice, insure domestic tranquility [peace], provide for the common defense, promote the general welfare, and secure the blessings of liberty to ourselves and our posterity [future generations], do ordain and establish this Constitution for the United States of America.

First Amendment (1791)

Congress shall make no law respecting an establishment of religion, or prohibiting the free exercise thereof; or abridging [limiting] the freedom of speech, or of the press; or the right of the people peaceably to assemble, and to petition the government for a redress [correction] of grievances.

A Snapshot From History ■■■■■■■■■■■■■■

After the colonists declared their independence from Great Britain, they needed to form their own government. The colonists didn't want to have a king or a government like the one in Great Britain. They also didn't want a government that was more powerful than the people it represented. The colonists chose to form a **republic**, in which citizens elect people to represent them in government.

In 1777, the Articles of Confederation was written. The colonists soon realized that this document didn't give the national government enough power. In 1787, representatives from almost every state gathered at a meeting called the Constitutional **Convention**. There they wrote a Constitution. However, not everyone was pleased with this document. So, the writers of the Constitution included a process for amending, or changing, the document. In 1791, the first ten **amendments,** known as the **Bill of Rights**, were added to the Constitution. Today, there are 27 amendments to the Constitution.

Terms To Know ≡

republic
> a government that takes its power from the people, who elect its leaders

convention
> an official gathering

amendments
> changes to a document

Bill of Rights
> the first ten amendments to the U.S. Constitution

Primary-Source Questions

Use your knowledge of social studies and your American History textbook to help you analyze the historical document.

Multiple Choice

Read each item carefully. Circle the number of the correct answer.

1. **Identify the document.**

    1   The Constitution of the United States

    2   The Constitution of the Confederacy of Southern States

    3   The constitution for each state of the Union

    4   The constitution with different laws for each state

2. **"We the people," means that**

    1   the states would run the government.

    2   the government would control the people.

    3   the government would be run by and for the people.

    4   the Founding Fathers would run the government.

3. **What is the purpose of the First Amendment to the Constitution?**

    1   To protect certain personal freedoms

    2   To prevent the Constitution from being ratified

    3   To strengthen the power of the government

    4   To expand the powers of the government

4. **Which of the following actions does the First Amendment NOT protect?**

    1   The right to join a club and meet with other students

    2   The right to read and write a school newspaper

    3   The right to practice your religion

    4   The right to vote for an unpopular candidate

Essay

Write your essay on a separate sheet of paper.

Identify each of the rights protected by the First Amendment. Give at least one example of how you exercise each right in your everyday life.

Test Tip

★ Before you read the passage, scan the questions. This will help you focus on the key points.

Practice 2
Analyzing Historical Documents

The Mayflower Compact

Here is the Mayflower Compact. Read *A Snapshot From History*. It will provide historical background for the document.

The Mayflower Compact (1620)

In the name of God, Amen. We, whose names are underwritten, the loyal subjects of our dread sovereign Lord, King James, by the grace of God, of Great Britain, France, and Ireland King, Defender of the Faith, etc.

Having undertaken, for the glory of God, and advancement of the Christian faith, and honor of our King and country, a voyage to plant the first colony in the northern parts of Virginia, do by these presents solemnly and mutually, in the presence of God, and one another, covenant [promise] and combine our selves together into a civil body politic; for our better ordering and preservation [protection] and further-ance of the ends aforesaid; and by virtue hereof to enact, constitute, and frame such just and equal laws, ordinances [laws], acts, constitu-tions and offices, from time to time, as shall be thought most meet [fitting] and convenient for the general good of the Colony, unto which we promise all due submission and obedience.

In witness whereof we have hereunder subscribed [signed] our names at Cape Cod the eleventh of November, in the year of the reign of our sovereign lord, King James, of England, France, and Ireland the eigh-teenth, and of Scotland the fiftie-fourth, Anno Dominie, 1620.

A Snapshot From History

By the early 1600s, a small group of people called **Puritans** wanted to leave England and move to a new land where they were free to follow their own religious beliefs. They decided to make their new home in America. In 1620, they set sail on a ship called the *Mayflower*. They were joined by other peo-ple hoping to make a better life in this country. Together, they became known as the **Pilgrims**.

When the Pilgrims landed in America 65 days after they had set sail, they realized they needed a form of government. While still aboard the ship, they drafted a document called the Mayflower **Compact**.

Terms To Know

Puritan
a member of a religious group that wanted to simplify the practices of the Church of England

Pilgrim
a person who travels to a new land

compact
a formal agreement

Primary-Source Questions

Use your knowledge of social studies and your American History textbook to help you analyze the historical document.

Constructed Response

Read each question carefully. Write your answer on the lines provided.

1. **What day and year was the Mayflower Compact signed?**

    _____

2. **According to the document, why did the Pilgrims leave England?**

    _____

    _____

3. **What was the purpose of the Mayflower Compact?**

    _____

    _____

4. **For whom was the Mayflower Compact written?**

    _____

    _____

5. **Why did the Pilgrims feel that this compact was necessary?**

    _____

    _____

    _____

Essay

Write your essay on a separate sheet of paper.

You are one of the Pilgrims landing in America. Write the Mayflower Compact in your own words. Then, explain your reasons for writing the document.

Gettysburg Address

Here is the Gettysburg Address. Read *A Snapshot From History.*
It will provide historical background for the speech.

From Abraham Lincoln, Gettysburg Address (1863)

Four score and seven years ago our fathers brought forth on this continent a new nation, conceived in liberty and dedicated to the proposition [idea] that all men are created equal. Now we are engaged in a great civil war, testing whether that nation or any nation so conceived and so dedicated can long endure. We are met on a great battlefield of that war. We have come to dedicate a portion of that field as a final resting-place for those who here gave their lives that that nation might live. It is altogether fitting and proper that we should do this. . . . The world will little note nor long remember what we say here, but it can never forget what they did here. . . . It is rather for us to be here dedicated to the great task remaining before us—that from these honored dead we take increased devotion to that cause for which they gave the last full measure of devotion—that we here highly resolve that these dead shall not have died in vain, that this nation under God shall have a new birth of freedom, and that government of the people, by the people, for the people, shall not perish [die] from the earth.

A Snapshot From History ▪▪▪▪▪▪▪▪▪▪▪▪▪▪▪▪▪▪▪▪

In 1863, the **Civil War** between the North and the South was raging. Under the command of General Robert E. Lee, the **Confederate** army looked strong. However, General Lee knew that to win the war, he needed to win a large battle in the North, forcing the **Union** army to surrender. Lee's opportunity came on July 1, 1863, at Gettysburg, Pennsylvania. The bloody Battle of Gettysburg lasted three days, and General Lee's army was badly defeated.

More than 50,000 men on both sides were wounded or lost their lives in this battle. Four months later, on November 9, 1863, President Abraham Lincoln delivered a speech at the dedication of a cemetery for the soldiers who died in the Gettysburg battle.

Terms To Know ≡

Civil War
a war between people of the same country

Confederate
southern

Union
northern

Primary-Source Questions

Use your knowledge of social studies and your American History textbook to help you analyze the speech.

Constructed Response

Read each question carefully. Write your answer on the lines provided.

1. **President Lincoln gave this speech in 1863. Which year did he refer to when he said, "Four score and seven years ago…"? (Hint: *Score* means "a set of twenty.")**

   _____

2. **President Lincoln quoted a document that said, "all men are created equal." From what historical document did this famous phrase come?**

   _____

3. **Why do you think Lincoln quoted this phrase in this particular speech?**

   _____

   _____

   _____

4. **What is the main idea of the speech?**

   _____

   _____

   _____

Essay

Write your essay on a separate sheet of paper.

Explain what Lincoln promised in the last sentence of the Gettysburg Address.

Analyzing Historical Documents

John F. Kennedy's Inaugural Address

Here are a few passages from John F. Kennedy's inaugural address. Read *A Snapshot From History*. It will provide historical background for the speech.

From John F. Kennedy, Inaugural Address (1961)

. . . Let every nation know, whether it wishes us well or ill, that we shall pay any price, bear any burden, meet any hardship, support any friend, oppose any foe [enemy], in order to assure the survival and the success of liberty. . . .

. . . In your hands, my fellow citizens, more than in mine, will rest the final success or failure of our course. Since this country was founded, each generation of Americans has been summoned to give testimony [proof] to its national loyalty. The graves of young Americans who answered the call to service surround the globe. . . .

. . . Now the trumpet summons us again—not as a call to bear arms [fight in the military], though arms we need; not as a call to battle, though embattled we are—but a call to bear the burden of a long twilight struggle, year in and year out . . . a struggle against the common enemies of man: tyranny [unjust use of power], poverty, disease, and war itself. . . .

. . . And so, my fellow Americans: ask not what your country can do for you—ask what you can do for your country. My fellow citizens of the world: ask not what America will do for you, but what together we can do for the freedom of man. . . .

A Snapshot From History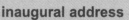

In July 1960, the Democratic National Convention chose John Fitzgerald Kennedy as their presidential candidate. Kennedy ran an energetic campaign against Richard Nixon, giving more than 300 speeches. He discussed his goals for changing American ideas about the country and the world. His vision for the United States became known as the New Frontier. Kennedy wanted American citizens to become more involved in the government and the world. Kennedy won the presidential election and became President on January 20, 1961. His **inaugural address** was brief, but powerful.

Term To Know ≣

inaugural address
a speech that an elected official gives when inducted or admitted into office

Primary-Source Questions

Use your knowledge of social studies and your American History textbook to help you analyze the speech.

Multiple Choice

Read each item carefully. Circle the number of the correct answer.

1. **In his speech, Kennedy asked that Americans join together to do all of the following, except**

    1   fight against poverty and disease.

    2   promote peace.

    3   defend freedom.

    4   declare war on enemies.

2. **Kennedy wanted other nations to know that the people of the United States would**

    1   do anything to assure the success of freedom.

    2   respond to the call to bear arms.

    3   ask what we can do for the freedom of man.

    4   fight in a war if there was a good reason.

3. **When Kennedy said, "Ask not what your country can do for you—ask what you can do for your country," he wanted Americans to**

    1   call their local government officials to suggest how the government needs to change.

    2   rely on the government to make changes.

    3   give testimony to national loyalty.

    4   take an active role to make the country a better place.

Essay

Write your essay on a separate sheet of paper.

Explain what Kennedy meant in the final paragraph of his speech. Give examples of what American citizens can do for the country.

Hands-On Activity

In this chapter, you have read historical documents that protect all Americans' rights to certain personal freedoms. In addition, you have read speeches by Americans who have fought to protect these freedoms. Using magazines and newspapers, make a collage of pictures, headlines, and articles that illustrate these freedoms. Share your collage with your class.

Model Lesson: President Andrew Jackson

⭐ Here's the Skill ⬇

Did you know that cartoons are sometimes called "the funnies"? That is because cartoons are drawn in a funny or humorous way and often make us laugh. Political cartoons are usually about government or politics. They often comment on a person or event in the news. Political cartoons give an opinion, or belief, about a current issue. They sometimes use caricatures to exaggerate a person or thing in order to express a point of view. Like editorials, political cartoons try to persuade people to see things in a certain way.

Where have you seen a political cartoon? If you said, "in a newspaper or magazine," you are absolutely right! Political cartoons have been popular in the United States since the 1700s. They date back to the days of Benjamin Franklin, when the colonies were struggling for independence from Great Britain. Until the 1880s, political cartoons were usually found in weekly or monthly publications. That is because they took a long time to make. Each cartoon was engraved, or carved, into a piece of wood in order to print it on paper.

Today, political cartoons can be found in daily newspapers. Using a photo engraving method, cartoons can be copied very quickly. If something important happens in the news—and a cartoonist acts quickly—a cartoon can often influence the public.

 Here's Why ☒

In addition to news articles and broadcasts, political cartoons offer yet another perspective, or outlook, on a current event. Being able to analyze a political cartoon will help you to better understand different points of view about issues during a particular time period.

Read *A Snapshot From History*. It will provide historical background for the political cartoon on page 18.

A Snapshot From History ■■■■■■■■■■■■■■■■■■■■

After breaking free from Great Britain and declaring their independence in 1776, Americans had to determine what kind of government they wanted. They didn't want a king. They didn't want a government that was more powerful than the people it represented.

People disagreed about what the new government should be like. Americans compromised, or worked through their differences, and eventually created the U.S. Constitution. Then, the Bill of Rights was added to the Constitution. These first ten amendments protected Americans and guaranteed them many freedoms, such as freedom of speech.

In 1828, Andrew Jackson was elected President. Some critics questioned his loyalty to the Constitution. For example, Jackson ignored a **Supreme Court** decision and removed the Cherokee people from their lands. In addition, Jackson put many of his friends and supporters in key government positions.

People began to wonder if Jackson was really a "man of the people." He seemed to be forcing his own views on the United States.

Term To Know ≣

Supreme Court
the highest court in the United States

Look at the following cartoon. It is a humorous comment on how some people viewed President Jackson.

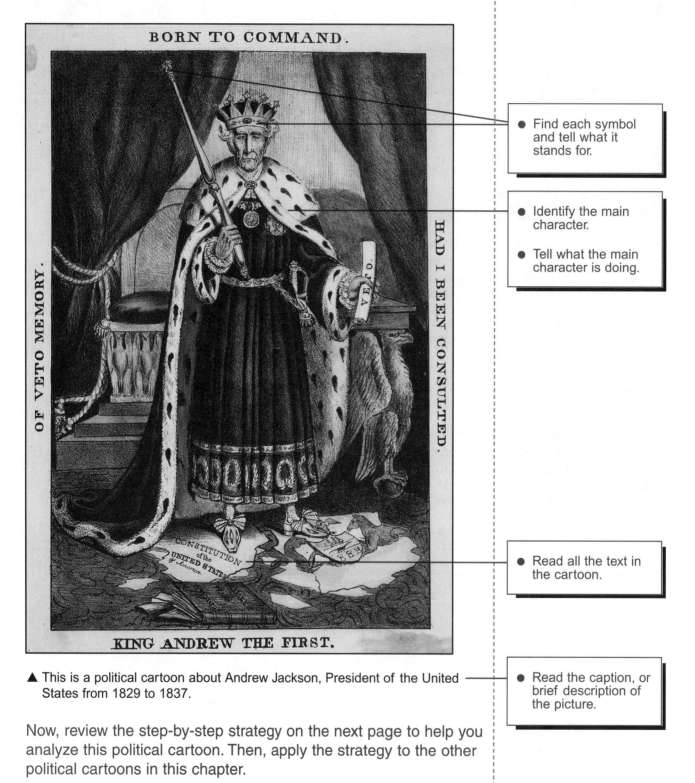

- Find each symbol and tell what it stands for.

- Identify the main character.

- Tell what the main character is doing.

- Read all the text in the cartoon.

▲ This is a political cartoon about Andrew Jackson, President of the United States from 1829 to 1837.

- Read the caption, or brief description of the picture.

Now, review the step-by-step strategy on the next page to help you analyze this political cartoon. Then, apply the strategy to the other political cartoons in this chapter.

1. Read and Study

★ Pay attention to every detail of the drawing. Find each symbol and determine what it stands for.

★ Determine who the main character is and what he or she is doing.

★ Read the words in the cartoon. They often express the cartoonist's opinion of the issue.

★ Read the caption or description of the picture. It helps place the cartoon in a historical context.

★ Write down any words you do not know. Then, look them up in a dictionary.

2. Ask Yourself Questions

Answer the following questions about the cartoon on page 18.

1. Who is the main character? What is he doing?

_____

_____

2. List two symbols in the cartoon. What does each symbol stand for?

_____

_____

3. What is the main idea of the cartoon?

_____

_____

4. What do you think is the cartoonist's opinion of Jackson?

_____

_____

3. Put It All Together

Describe how the cartoon reflects how some Americans viewed President Jackson. Include the cartoonist's opinion.

Lincoln Rebuilds the Union

Here is a political cartoon about Abraham Lincoln at the end of the Civil War. Read *A Snapshot From History*. It will provide historical background for the cartoon.

▲ This political cartoon shows Abraham Lincoln trying to repair the Union.

A Snapshot From History ▪▪▪▪▪▪▪▪▪▪▪▪▪▪▪▪▪▪

The Civil War was fought between the South (or the Confederacy) and the North (or the Union) from 1861 to 1865. The period after the Civil War is called **Reconstruction**. During this time, the U.S. government tried to reunite, or join together again, the former Confederacy with the Union.

Before the war ended, President Lincoln had already begun his plan to reunite the divided country. In his plan, most former Confederates could receive a pardon by taking an oath of loyalty to the Union. Some people disagreed with Lincoln's plan and wanted to punish the South for breaking away from the Union. As a result, Lincoln and Congress could not reach an agreement.

Term To Know ≡

Reconstruction
the period from 1865–1877, in which programs were created to reunite the South with the North

Primary-Source Questions

Use your knowledge of social studies and your American History textbook to help you analyze the political cartoon.

Constructed Response

Read each question carefully. Write your answer on the lines provided.

1. **Who is the main character?**

   _____

2. **What is the main character doing?**

   _____

   _____

3. **List two symbols that you see. What do they stand for?**

   _____

   _____

   _____

   _____

4. **What is the main idea of this cartoon?**

   _____

   _____

   _____

   _____

Essay

Write your essay on a separate sheet of paper.

What message does the cartoonist express about this time in history? How do the symbols in the cartoon support this message?

Analyzing Political Cartoons

President Hoover and the Great Depression

Here is a political cartoon about the Great Depression. Read *A Snapshot From History.* It will provide historical background for the cartoon.

▲ President Herbert Hoover is telling the dog, "You stop following me, d'hear!"

A Snapshot From History

On October 29, 1929, the stock market in the United States crashed. The crash marked the end of a prosperous decade and the beginning of a long period of hard economic times known as the Great **Depression**. By 1932, one out of every four Americans was unemployed.

Many Americans blamed the President, Herbert Hoover, for the country's problems. Americans wanted Hoover and the government to help them through the economic crisis and end the Depression. However, President Hoover thought that local and private groups, not the government, should help people in need. He tried to make it easier for people and businesses to help themselves. He cut taxes and asked business leaders not to lay off workers or lower their wages. However, business leaders did not cooperate. Nothing Hoover did seemed to work. Many families lost their homes and ran out of money. Americans began to think that Hoover didn't care about their problems.

Term To Know

depression
a long period of economic problems

Primary-Source Questions

Use your knowledge of social studies and your American History textbook to help you analyze the political cartoon.

Multiple Choice

Read each item carefully. Circle the number of the correct answer.

1. **What does the dog represent in the cartoon?**

   1 The Great Depression

   2 People who are hungry

   3 Hoover's presidency

   4 The government

2. **The way Hoover is dressed shows that**

   1 he is a member of Congress.

   2 he is a middle-class American.

   3 he is a leader who is concerned about the poor.

   4 he is economically secure and a friend of the wealthy.

3. **Hoover distances himself from the dog because**

   1 he wants to help Americans.

   2 he wants to run for re-election.

   3 he does not want to be blamed for the Depression.

   4 he does not like to solve problems.

4. **What is the cartoonist's opinion of Hoover?**

   1 Hoover's policies created the Depression.

   2 Hoover's policies helped to end the Depression.

   3 Hoover was not doing anything to end the Depression.

   4 Hoover would rather help people than dogs.

Essay

Write your essay on a separate sheet of paper.

Describe how the cartoon reflects what was happening in the United States during Hoover's presidency.

Analyzing Political Cartoons

Dr. Martin Luther King Jr.

Here is a political cartoon about Dr. Martin Luther King Jr. and the civil rights movement. Read *A Snapshot From History*. It will provide historical background for the cartoon.

▲ This is a political cartoon about Dr. Martin Luther King Jr. and the civil rights movement.

A Snapshot From History ▮▮▮▮▮▮▮▮▮▮▮▮▮▮▮▮▮▮▮

Dr. Martin Luther King Jr. was an important leader of the civil rights movement from the mid-1950s until his death in 1968. He fought for the rights of African Americans. King believed that all people should be treated equally.

King worked to end **segregation** using nonviolent methods. He and his followers held peaceful marches, **sit-ins**, **boycotts**, and Freedom Rides to fight against unfair laws. In 1963, King led a march on Washington, D.C., where he gave his famous *I Have a Dream* speech to more than 200,000 people. In his speech, King spoke about his dream for racial harmony and equality. In 1964, he received the Nobel Peace Prize for bringing about change without violence. Dr. King was assassinated on April 4, 1968.

Terms To Know ☰

segregation
separation of the races

sit-in
a protest in which people refuse to leave a place

boycott
a protest in which people refuse to buy products or use services

Primary-Source Questions

Use your knowledge of social studies and your American History textbook to help you analyze the political cartoon.

Constructed Response

Read each question carefully. Write your answer on the lines provided.

1. **What is the title of the cartoon?**

   _____

2. **What dream does the title refer to?**

   _____

   _____

3. **List two symbols in the cartoon.**

   _____

   _____

4. **What do these symbols stand for?**

   _____

   _____

5. **According to the cartoon, who are the enemies of the dream?**

   _____

   _____

Essay

Write your essay on a separate sheet of paper.

Does the cartoon suggest that there is hope for King's dream? Use details from the cartoon to support your answer.

Saving the Environment

The following two cartoons are both warnings to save the environment. The cartoon on the left was published in 1970, while the cartoon on the right was published in 1986. Read *A Snapshot From History.* It will provide historical background for the cartoons.

▲ These political cartoons are about the environment.

A Snapshot From History

Imagine a world where people wear gas masks because the air quality is so unhealthy. Many Americans have grown more concerned about the harmful effects of the growth of industry on the environment. **Acid rain** and deforestation are two examples of environmental problems.

People have realized that natural resources, such as land, air, water, and energy need to be protected. Americans are discovering that they need to limit their use of these resources.

Politicians have had difficulty proposing measures to help the environment, often because of cost. However, there are many private and government-run organizations, such as the **Environmental Protection Agency** or EPA, that work to protect the environment or that educate people about how to care for the environment.

Terms To Know

acid rain
rain containing acids formed by pollutants from burning fossil fuels

Environmental Protection Agency
government-run organization that works to protect the environment

Primary-Source Questions

Use your knowledge of social studies and your American History textbook to help you analyze the political cartoons.

Multiple Choice

Read each item carefully. Circle the number of the correct answer.

1. **The figure in the cartoon on the left refers to a famous sculpture called *The Thinker*. Who does *The Thinker* stand for in the cartoon?**

   1 A smart person

   2 Man, or all people in society

   3 The President of the United States

   4 A conservationist

2. **The skeleton in the cartoon on the right represents**

   1 factories and industry.

   2 labor.

   3 the Environmental Protection Agency.

   4 people harmed by acid rain.

3. **Both of these cartoons make the criticism that**

   1 the government is stopping people from protecting the environment.

   2 the government should be more involved in environmental issues.

   3 environmental issues are not being actively addressed.

   4 the Environmental Protection Agency's biggest concern should be cleaning up the environment.

Essay

Write your essay on a separate sheet of paper.

Identify at least four features of the cartoons that symbolize the seriousness of the environmental problem. Explain each feature.

Hands-On Activity

Check newspapers, magazines, and the Internet for political cartoons. Then, draw your own political cartoon that reflects your opinion on an issue. Be sure to write a caption, a title, and other text that supports your opinion. Share your cartoon with your class.

Model Lesson: The Great Plains

⭐ Here's the Skill ⬇

Many advertisements are printed as posters. For example, when you go to the movie theater, you can see posters that advertise upcoming films. During election time, you may see posters that include photographs of candidates. You may even have created your own poster about a concert or sports event that is going to happen at your school.

Advertisements are also printed in magazines and newspapers and on billboards. These ads are written to convince people to buy products—from running shoes and cars to shampoo and hamburgers! Think about how many pages of ads you have to turn before finding the magazine article that you want to read. Companies place many ads hoping that you will grow familiar with their products and eventually decide to buy them.

In this chapter, you will be working with advertisements from the past. Just like today's advertisements, these ads were printed to give information, persuade buyers, and draw interest.

Here's Why

Historical advertisements provide information about events or products. By reading these advertisements, you can learn many things about what people were doing and buying many years ago.

Read *A Snapshot From History*. It will provide historical background for the advertisement on page 30.

A Snapshot From History

In the mid-to-late 1800s, many Americans were eager to move west. Although they knew hard work awaited them, they were looking for a better way of life. Advertisements for land helped attract people to the Great Plains, the area between the Mississippi River and the Rocky Mountains.

In 1862, Congress passed the Homestead Act. It promised men who were at least 21 years old 160 free acres of land. The men had to live on the **prairie** and farm it for five years. Then in 1869, the first **transcontinental** railroad was completed. The railroad made it easier for Americans to travel west. By the 1870s, thousands of people seeking a new life began moving onto the Great Plains. Millions of acres of grassland were turned into farms.

Although ads promised cheap land and fertile soil, they did not warn settlers of the harsh prairie life. Farmers faced extreme weather conditions, natural disasters, and economic hardship. Many discouraged farmers eventually moved back to the East. For those people who chose to remain, life on the prairie involved a great deal of hard work and determination.

Terms To Know

prairie
the flat, rolling land of the Great Plains

transcontinental
across a continent

Here's How ⩡

Look at the following poster. It is advertising the sale of land in 1874 in order to attract people to the Great Plains.

▲ This advertisement for land appeared in 1874.

● Look at the artwork. What does the picture show?

● Read all the words to determine what the poster is advertising.

● Determine the audience for the advertisement.

● Read the caption. It provides historical context.

Now, review the step-by-step strategy on the next page to help you analyze this advertisement. Then, apply the strategy to the other ads in this chapter.

1. Read and Study

★ Pay attention to every detail in the advertisement. Look for answers to the questions *Who? What? When? Where?* and *Why?*

★ Determine the main idea of the advertisement by reading all slogans, or phrases, and by studying the artwork.

★ Determine the audience. Identify the people who the advertisement is intended to reach.

★ Read the caption to place the advertisement in a historical context.

★ Write any words you don't know. Then, check them in a dictionary.

2. Ask Yourself Questions

Answer the following questions about the advertisement on page 30.

1. **What is the advertisement about?**

   _____

2. **When is it happening?**

   _____

3. **Where is it happening?**

   _____

4. **Who is the intended audience?**

   _____

   _____

5. **Why is the land being advertised?**

   _____

   _____

   _____

3. Put It All Together

Describe how the poster reflects what was happening in the United States during the mid-to-late 1800s.

Practice 1
Analyzing Advertisements

African Slave Trade

Here is an advertisement about the sale of Africans by slave traders. Read *A Snapshot From History.* It will provide historical background for the advertisement.

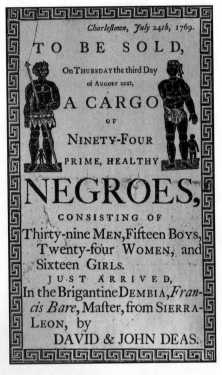

▲ The sale of Africans was common in the Southern colonies.

A Snapshot From History

In the late 1600s, the economy of the Southern **colonies** relied on the labor of enslaved Africans. **Plantation** owners needed workers to plant and harvest their tobacco crops. African people were taken from their homelands and forced onto slave ships.

The Africans suffered terribly from hunger, thirst, and disease on the long journey to America. Many became sick or died because of the filthy, cramped conditions. When they arrived in America, they were auctioned, or sold to the highest bidder.

Many slave traders became rich by selling thousands of Africans into slavery. By the late 1700s, there were about 500,000 enslaved Africans in the Southern colonies.

Terms To Know

colonies
settlements in a distant land that are governed by another country

plantation
a large farm requiring many workers

Primary-Source Questions

Use your knowledge of social studies and your American History textbook to help you analyze the advertisement.

Multiple Choice

Read each item carefully. Circle the number of the correct answer.

1. **The enslaved Africans were transported from**
   1 America to Sierra Leon.
   2 Sierra Leon to America.
   3 the North to Charleston.
   4 Charleston to the North.

2. **Who is the audience for this advertisement?**
   1 Plantation owners
   2 Slave traders
   3 Africans
   4 David and John Deas

3. **What does the advertisement tell you about the sale?**
   1 There were children for sale.
   2 The Africans were considered fierce fighters.
   3 There were women for sale.
   4 All of the above.

4. **What can you tell from the advertisement about the way enslaved Africans were treated?**
   1 Enslaved Africans were comfortable on the journey.
   2 Enslaved Africans were treated as property, not as humans.
   3 None of the Africans were sick.
   4 Only the best Africans of the cargo were for sale.

Essay

Write your essay on a separate sheet of paper.

How does the African slave trade contradict the belief that all men are created equal? What details from the poster support your answer?

Test Tip

★ The answer to a question isn't always stated in an ad. However, you should be able to infer the answer from the information given. Making inferences is part of analyzing primary sources.

Practice 2
Analyzing Advertisements

The Presidential Campaign of 1864

Here is an advertisement for the presidential campaign of 1864. Read *A Snapshot From History*. It will provide historical background for the advertisement.

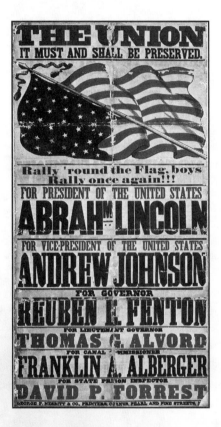

◀ This presidential campaign poster appeared in 1864.

A Snapshot From History

Before the end of the Civil War, President Lincoln created a plan to reunite the Union. Although Lincoln was a Republican, there were many Republicans in Congress who did not support him. They thought that his plan did not punish the former Confederates in the South enough. Even some **moderate** Republicans thought his plan was not harsh enough.

The tension between Lincoln and members of Congress grew. Many thought that Lincoln would not receive the **presidential nomination** of the Republican Party, known as the Union Party during the 1864 election. In the end, Lincoln won both the nomination and the election.

Terms To Know

moderate
having mild, reasonable opinions

presidential nomination
the naming of a person by a political party to be a candidate in a presidential election

Primary-Source Questions

Use your knowledge of social studies and your American History textbook to help you analyze the advertisement.

Constructed Response

Read each question carefully. Write your answer on the lines provided.

1. **Who was Lincoln's running mate for Vice President during the 1864 election?**

   _____

2. **What do you think is the meaning of the slogan "Rally 'round the flag boys, Rally once again!!!"**

   _____

   _____

3. **What was Lincoln's main message on the campaign poster?**

   _____

   _____

4. **Do you think this poster was shown all around the nation? Explain.**

   _____

   _____

5. **How does the symbol of the flag support Lincoln's re-election campaign?**

   _____

   _____

Essay

Write your essay on a separate sheet of paper.

According to the poster, how did the Civil War affect the nation's politics in 1864?

The *Lusitania* and World War I

Here is a poster advertising a journey on the *Lusitania*. Read
A Snapshot From History. It will provide historical background for
the advertisement.

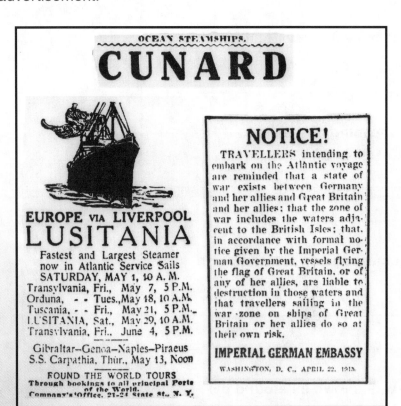

▲ This poster is an advertisement for travel on the *Lusitania*.

A Snapshot From History

In 1914, World War I broke out among the nations of Europe. As
battles raged, the United States tried to stay out of the conflict.
However, in 1915, the German government warned Americans that
German ships would sink any enemy ship coming to or going from
Great Britain.

Official notices warned travelers on the *Lusitania*, a British passenger ship, about this danger in the war zone. Then, on May 7, 1915,
a German submarine sank the *Lusitania*, killing 1,198 people. Of
those killed, 128 were Americans. The sinking of the *Lusitania* was
one incident that led the United States to declare war against
Germany in 1917.

Primary-Source Questions

Use your knowledge of social studies and your American History textbook to help you analyze the advertisement.

Multiple Choice

Read each item carefully. Circle the number of the correct answer.

1. **The *Lusitania* was sailing**

   1 on a Pacific voyage.

   2 on an Atlantic voyage.

   3 from Liverpool via Europe.

   4 only to Gibraltar, Genoa, and Naples.

2. **When was the *Lusitania* supposed to leave port?**

   1 Saturday, May 29, 10:00 A.M.

   2 Friday, May 7, 5:00 P.M.

   3 Tuesday, May 18, 10:00 A.M.

   4 Saturday, May 1, 10:00 A.M.

3. **Who was the intended audience?**

   1 Germans

   2 Americans

   3 The British navy

   4 The U.S. government

4. **Why would the Imperial German Embassy print a warning on American advertisements?**

   1 They wanted the United States to enter the war.

   2 They did not want to kill Americans.

   3 They did not want to take responsibility for American deaths.

   4 They did not want the United States to enter the war.

Essay

Write your essay on a separate sheet of paper.

Whose responsibility is it to keep civilians safe during a war? Use the *Lusitania* voyage as an example.

Women and the War Effort

Here are two posters about women and their efforts during World War II. Read *A Snapshot From History*. It will provide historical background for the posters.

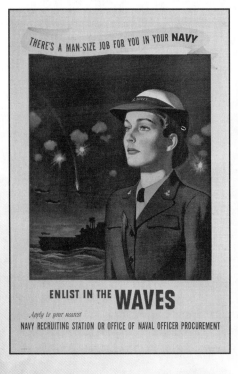

▲ Women were important to both the military and industry during World War II.

A Snapshot From History

During Word War II, American women became an important part of the **workforce**. American men were away fighting the war or working in factories and on farms. Therefore, many war-related jobs were filled by women. They helped to build airplanes, tanks, ships, guns, and bombs. Almost half of all American women took some type of job during the war.

Women also served in the armed forces during the war. About 350,000 served their country. More than 140,000 joined the WAC (Women's Army Corps). Another 100,000 joined the Navy WAVES (Women Accepted for Volunteer Emergency Service). Many women also served in the Marine Corps and the Coast Guard. Women showed the world that they could move beyond the traditional roles of housewife and mother.

Term To Know

workforce
total number of people employed in a nation

Primary-Source Questions

Use your knowledge of social studies and your American History textbook to help you analyze the advertisements.

Constructed Response

Read each question carefully. Write your answer on the lines provided.

1. **Who is the intended audience of these ads?**

   _____

2. **How are the women portrayed in each poster?**

   _____

   _____

3. **What features of the ad on the left would attract women during the war?**

   _____

   _____

   _____

4. **What features of the ad on the right would attract women during the war?**

   _____

   _____

5. **How do you think the pictures of these women differed from how women were viewed before the war?**

   _____

   _____

Essay

Write your essay on a separate sheet of paper.

If the armed services wanted to enlist your help today, how would you respond to the following slogan? "There is a man-size job for you in your Navy." Do you think women and men would feel differently?

Hands-On Activity

Choose an issue about which you feel strongly. Create an advertisement to "sell" your ideas and influence your readers. Include words and images. Share your advertisement with your class.

Firsthand Accounts

Model Lesson: Autobiography from World War I

⭐Here's the Skill ▼

In this chapter, you will analyze firsthand accounts by both famous Americans and ordinary citizens. They include autobiographies, letters, and eyewitness accounts. All of these firsthand accounts help us learn about people and events from the past.

You have probably written about yourself and your own experiences in a diary or journal. For some, this type of writing grows into an autobiography, the complete story of a person's life written by that person. Autobiographies can be important sources of information about world events.

Letters are also important firsthand accounts. They are messages written by one person and sent to another. Letters help us understand how events were experienced by the people involved. For example, we can learn a great deal about our nation's history by reading the letters from Presidents and their wives.

Eyewitness accounts are spoken or written. When you tune in to a news show, you may hear a reporter interviewing several people on the street about an event that just occurred. Eyewitness accounts bring an event to life by relating individual experiences of it.

# Here's Why

Think of an event or period in history that interests you. Now consider how valuable it would be to read material written by someone who actually lived through the event or period. Firsthand accounts will add to your understanding of why things happened and how people felt about them.

Read *A Snapshot From History*. It will provide historical background about the firsthand account on page 42.

A Snapshot From History

When the United States entered World War I in 1917, the nation needed many soldiers. Some men volunteered for the army, while others were **drafted**, or chosen for military service. Soon the United States had a large armed force. American troops made a difference in the war. They helped Great Britain and its allies gain the advantage and win the war.

Captain Eddie Rickenbacker was a fighter pilot who was one of the commanders of the 94th "Hat-in-the-Ring" **Squadron**. The job of these pilots was extremely dangerous and called for great skill. They were responsible for striking targets on the ground as well as fighting against enemy airplanes in the air. Rickenbacker's unit of pilots had the highest number of air victories of any American squadron.

Terms To Know

drafted
required to serve in a nation's armed forces for a specific period

squadron
a unit of air force fighter pilots

Here's How ▼

Read the following passage from Captain Eddie Rickenbacker's autobiography, *Fighting the Flying Circus*. It tells about a day when he and his squadron fought against German forces during World War I.

From Fighting the Flying Circus by Captain Eddie Rickenbacker

● Identify the title and the author.

Hastily getting out of doors, I looked over the dark sky, wondering as I did so how many of our boys it would claim before this day's work was done! For we had an important part to play in this day's operations. Headquarters had sent us orders to attack all the enemy observation [spy] balloons until infantry's operations were completed. . . . The safety of thousands of our attacking soldiers depended upon our success in eliminating [removing] these all-watching eyes of the enemy. . . .

● Identify the main idea of the account.

I was the last to leave the field, getting off the ground at exactly 5:20. It was still dark and we had to have the searchlights turned onto the field for a moment to see the ground while we took off. As soon as we lifted into the darkness the lights were extinguished [turned off]. . . . I saw directly ahead of me the long snaky flashes of enemy tracer bullets from the ground piercing the sky. There was the location of my balloon and either Cook or Chambers was already attacking it. The enemy had discovered them and were putting up the usual hail of flaming projectiles [objects hurled up, such as a bullet] around the balloon site. . . . Even before the glare of the first had died I saw our second enemy balloon go up in flames. My pilots had succeeded beyond my fondest expectations.

● Determine the setting —time and place—of the account.

● Determine the author's role in the event and his opinion of the event.

Now, review the strategy on the next page to help you analyze this account. Then, apply the strategy to the other firsthand accounts in this chapter.

1. Read and Study

★ Identify the title and the author of the account.

★ Use the title and details from the account to identify the main idea.

★ Read the account a few times. Determine the setting—time and place—of the account.

★ Identify the position, job, or role that the author held.

★ Identify the author's opinions, views, beliefs, or judgment about the situation.

★ Write down any words you do not know. Then, check them in a dictionary.

2. Ask Yourself Questions

Answer the following questions about the account on page 42.

1. What do you suppose the title means?

_____

_____

_____

2. What is the main idea of the passage?

_____

_____

3. What is the setting of the passage?

_____

4. Identify the role of the author in the event. What is his opinion of the event?

_____

_____

3. Put It All Together

Explain how this firsthand account gives information about American involvement in World War I.

Analyzing Firsthand Accounts

Letter by Abigail Adams

Here is a letter written by First Lady Abigail Adams to her daughter from the newly built White House. Read *A Snapshot From History*. It will provide historical background for the letter.

From Letter by Abigail Adams

Washington, 21 November, 1800

My Dear Child,

. . . The river, which runs up to Alexandria, is in full view of my window, and I see the vessels as they pass and repass. The house is upon a grand and superb scale . . . an establishment very well proportioned to the President's salary. . . .

And when asked how I like it, say that I write you the situation is beautiful, which is true. The house is made habitable [livable], but there is not a single apartment finished. . . . Upstairs there is the oval room, which is designed for the drawing room, and has the crimson furniture in it. It is a very handsome room now; but when completed, it will be beautiful. . . .

. . . Since I sat down to write, I have been called down to a servant from Mount Vernon, with a billet [letter] from Major Custis, and a haunch of venison, and a kind, congratulatory letter from Mrs. Lewis, upon my arrival in the city, with Mrs. Washington's love, inviting me to Mount Vernon, where, health permitting, I will go before I leave this place. . . .

Affectionately, your mother,

Abigail Adams

A Snapshot From History

Abigail Adams became the country's second **First Lady** when her husband John Adams became President in 1797. This was a position of honor that had its own special duties and responsibilities. Mrs. Adams was used to taking on many responsibilities, even before she became First Lady. For example, she managed the family farm in Massachusetts while her husband was away on government business.

While she was First Lady, Adams wrote many letters. In some of her letters, she expressed her beliefs about political issues. Other letters told of her personal experiences in the newly built White House in Washington, D.C.

Term To Know

First Lady
wife of the President, a governor, or a mayor

Primary-Source Questions

Use your knowledge of social studies and your American History textbook to help you analyze the letter.

Multiple Choice

Read each item carefully. Circle the number of the correct answer.

Test Tip

★ Read the multiple-choice answers carefully. Be sure that the number you choose answers the question directly. Some answers may be true, but may not answer the question.

1. **How does Adams describe the White House?**

   1 Newly renovated

   2 Carefully constructed

   3 Unfinished but habitable

   4 Finished except for the staircase

2. **Adams considers the President's salary**

   1 adequate

   2 inadequate

   3 more than enough

   4 extremely poor

3. **What is Adams's opinion of the White House?**

   1 She thinks it is a wonderful home.

   2 She thinks it will be beautiful someday.

   3 She thinks it should be more elegant since it is for a President.

   4 She thinks it is unpleasant.

4. **What can you tell about Adams's responsibilities from the third paragraph of the letter?**

   1 Adams leaves most responsibilities to her husband.

   2 Adams is in charge of preparing food at the White House.

   3 Adams has many social responsibilities as First Lady.

   4 Adams has no responsibilities.

Essay

Write your essay on a separate sheet of paper.

Describe the early construction of the White House based on the letter by Abigail Adams. What can you tell about the setting, the living conditions, and the comfort of the White House in its first years of construction?

Letters from the Civil War

Here are two letters written by soldiers during the Civil War. Read *A Snapshot From History*. It will provide historical background for the letter.

A Confederate Letter (1861)

Dear Wife,

We had another great battle on Sunday, it commenced [began] at 6 o'clock, it was the hardest battle that was ever fought in America. They had 10 to our one—we conquered them, we lost about 800. . . . The Yankees [Union soldiers] lost about 5,000 and we took 1,300 prisoners and 125 horses, baggage wagons and 64 pieces of cannon. I was not in the battle but could hear the report of the cannons which was in very plain view. I had to stand sentinel [duty] at the hospital door. I had to be up all night to guard the wounded —it was the saddest thing I ever saw to hear the moans of the wounded and dying. . . .

I am always thinking of you and the children. . . .

Joseph M. Elkins To: Sarah Elkins

A Union Letter (1864)

Dear Father,

I received your letter of the 12th inst. You have no idea how much good it does a soldier to get a letter from home. . . .

My health is excellent, we have had some very hard times. . . . The rainy weather and short rations have made a great many sick men. I have frequently had nothing for 36 hours but a cup of coffee and a few green apples.

We have had some fighting to do lately. Last Friday week [of] the 17th we attacked the rebel lines and drove them about 3 miles. On the evening of the twenty 2nd the rebels charged our lines but they went back faster than they came up. In two charges . . . on the 20th and 22nd, the rebs lost about 5 or 6 thousand men.

Well, I must close, give my love to all. Write often.

John Miller

A Snapshot From History

The Civil War was fought between the Confederate army from the South and the Union army from the North. Members of the same family often fought on different sides in the war. For example, one man from Ohio might face his cousin from Tennessee on opposing sides on the **battlefield**. Over the course of four years, more Americans would die fighting in the Civil War than in any other war in our nation's history.

Term To Know

battlefield
an area in which an armed combat is fought

Primary-Source Questions

Use your knowledge of social studies and your American History textbook to help you analyze the letter.

Multiple Choice

Read each item carefully. Circle the number of the correct answer.

1. **What role did the Confederate soldier play in the battle?**

   1 He fired the cannons.

   2 He treated the wounded soldiers.

   3 He guarded the wounded soldiers.

   4 He was the chaplain, or priest, for the army.

2. **How did the Confederate soldier seem to feel about the fighting that had occurred?**

   1 Sad but proud

   2 Relieved

   3 Overwhelmed

   4 Surprised

3. **From the Union soldier's perspective, how is the war progressing?**

   1 The Confederacy is winning.

   2 The soldiers have lost heart from the difficult conditions.

   3 The Rebels have fewer supplies than the Union.

   4 The Union is winning.

4. **Which of the following is not found in the letter from the Union soldier?**

   1 He is lonely for news from home.

   2 He is discouraged by the battles.

   3 He is in good health despite the rain.

   4 He is hungry from short rations.

Essay

Write your essay on a separate sheet of paper.

What can you tell about the life of a Civil War soldier from the letters?

Oral Account About Japanese Internment

Here is an oral account about life in a Japanese internment camp during World War II. Read *A Snapshot From History*. It will provide historical background for the account.

Told by Yuri Tateshi

It was terrible because you had to sell everything. Of course, we got nothing for it, because we had such a short time to go. The day before we left, we all slept on the floor, cooked on the floor, and ate on the floor.

When we first got to Manzanar [a Japanese internment camp], we were given numbers. We went to the mess hall [cafeteria], and we were given meals in tin plates and tin cups. It was canned hot dogs and canned spinach.

After eating, we were taken to our room. The floors were boarded, but you could see the ground below. What hurt most was seeing hay mattresses. We were used to a regular home. All of us were in one room. We felt like prisoners.

A Snapshot From History

Japan attacked Pearl Harbor, Hawaii, on December 7, 1941. The following day, the United States declared war on Japan. Some Americans were afraid that Japanese Americans living on the West Coast might be helping Japan. Newspapers and radio programs spread false reports that Japanese Americans were more loyal to Japan than to the United States.

In 1942, President Roosevelt ordered the removal of all Japanese Americans from their homes in California and areas of Arizona, Washington, and Oregon. More than 100,000 Japanese Americans were rounded up and moved to **internment camps**, where they were held against their will. Barbed wire and armed guards surrounded the camps.

Japanese Americans endured these conditions for almost four years. Yet, not a single Japanese American was ever found to have worked against the United States during the war.

Term To Know

internment camp
a place in which people are confined, especially during a time of war

Primary-Source Questions

Use your knowledge of social studies and your American History textbook to help you analyze the eyewitness account.

Constructed Response

Read each question carefully. Write your answer on the lines provided.

1. **Tateshi was sent to Manzanar. What was this place?**

   _____

   _____

2. **Why did Tateshi and her family sleep, cook, and eat on the floor the day before they left for Manzanar?**

   _____

   _____

3. **What can you tell about the way people were treated in Manzanar from the account?**

   _____

   _____

   _____

Test Tip

★ To better understand a question, restate it in your own words.

4. **What did Tateshi mean when she said, "We were used to a regular home"?**

   _____

   _____

5. **Why did Tateshi call herself and her family "prisoners"?**

   _____

   _____

Essay

Write your essay on a separate sheet of paper.

Based on the account, how were the rights of Japanese Americans violated by being sent to internment camps?

Practice 4
Analyzing Firsthand Accounts

Eyewitness Account About Desegregation

Here is an eyewitness account about the desegregation of Central High School in Little Rock, Arkansas, in 1957. Read *A Snapshot From History*. It will provide historical background for the account by Elizabeth Eckford, a student at the school.

From The Long Shadow of Little Rock
told by Elizabeth Eckford

Before I left home, Mother called us into the living room. She said we should have a word of prayer. Then I caught the bus and I got off a block from the school. I saw a large crowd of people standing across the street from the soldiers guarding Central. As I walked on, the crowd suddenly got very quiet. . . .

At the corner, I tried to pass through the long line of guards around the school so as to enter the grounds behind them. One of the guards pointed across the street. . . . So, I walked across the street conscious of the crowd that stood there, but they moved away from me.

Then someone shouted, "Here she comes, get ready!" I moved away from the crowd on the sidewalk and into the street. If the mob came at me, I could then cross back over so the guards could protect me.

The crowd moved in closer and then began to follow me, called me names. . . . Even so, I still wasn't too scared because all the time I kept thinking that the guards would protect me. . . . When I was able to steady my knees, I walked up to the guard who had let the white students in. He too didn't move. When I tried to squeeze past him, he raised his bayonet [rifle with a blade on the end] and then the other guards closed in and they raised their bayonets.

A Snapshot From History

In the 1950s and 1960s, the civil rights movement in the United States became very powerful. Civil rights leaders turned their attention to ending **segregated** schools. They demanded that all public schools be open to students of all races. The Supreme Court ordered schools to begin **desegregation**, but many schools still did not comply with the ruling.

In 1957, a federal court ordered Central High School in Little Rock, Arkansas, an all-white school, to enroll nine African American students. On the first day of school, the students faced an angry mob, and they were prevented from entering the school by the Arkansas National Guard. One of those nine students was Elizabeth Eckford.

Terms To Know

segregated
racially separated

desegregation
the abolishment of racial separation, especially in public schools

Primary-Source Questions

Use your knowledge of social studies and your American History textbook to help you analyze the firsthand account.

Constructed Response

Read each question carefully. Write your answer on the lines provided.

1. **What did Eckford see as she got off of the bus a block away from Central High School?**

   _____

   _____

2. **How did Eckford feel as she walked toward the school?**

   _____

   _____

3. **Why was the National Guard at the school?**

   _____

   _____

4. **How might Eckford have felt if she knew that the National Guard was not protecting her?**

   _____

   _____

5. **How did Eckford's actions show her commitment to the civil rights movement?**

   _____

   _____

Essay

Write your essay on a separate sheet of paper.

What can you tell about life in Little Rock, Arkansas, during the 1950s and 1960s from this account? Use details from the account to support your answer.

Hands-On Activity

Choose an event in the news that you feel strongly about or that has affected you personally. Write a letter in which you express your thoughts and opinions about the event. Share your letter with a classmate.

CHAPTER 5

Photographs and Paintings

Model Lesson: The Anasazi

 Here's the Skill

It is often said that "one picture is worth a thousand words." This saying means that one visual image can convey more information than many words can. For this reason photographs and paintings are important primary sources. They are a record of daily life, providing information about people, places, and events in history.

It's important to study a photograph carefully because it may contain a lot of information. Details, such as clothing, facial expressions, or objects, can tell you about the people in the photograph, the place it was taken, or a specific period in history.

Like photographs, paintings capture many details in a single image. An artist often reveals his or her own feelings about a subject or event in a painting. Look for clues about the artist's attitude in the details of the painting.

Here's Why ▼

Photography was invented in the 1800s. Before then, drawings and paintings were the only visual records of the past. Think of these pictures as a story. As a keen observer, you can gather important information about a time or event in history.

Read *A Snapshot From History*. It will provide historical background for the photograph on page 54.

A Snapshot From History ▪▪▪▪▪▪▪▪▪▪▪▪▪▪▪

The Anasazi were a group of Native Americans who lived in the Southwest, specifically in states we now call Arizona and New Mexico. They were hunters and gatherers who lived first in the mouths of caves or under rock overhangs. Later, from around A.D. 500 to 700, they became farmers and began to build houses in the sides of cliffs out of **adobe**. These **cliff dwellings** are now preserved as a national monument.

Archaeological evidence shows that the Anasazi created a highly developed culture. Researchers have found artifacts, such as pottery, baskets, jewelry, tools, and utensils that the Anasazi people used.

Descendants of the Anasazi were given the Spanish name Pueblo, meaning *village*, by the Spaniards who came to the Southwest many years later. The Pueblos adapted the Anasazi style of architecture and built their homes into the cliffs.

Terms To Know ≣

adobe
sun-dried bricks made of clay and straw

cliff dwellings
homes built into the sides of cliffs

archaeological evidence
signs used in the study of past life and cultures

Look at the following photograph of an Anasazi village built between A.D. 800 and 1100, in an area that is now part of Arizona.

▲ This is a photograph of an Anasazi village in Arizona. This village was 5 stories high and 70 feet wide.

- Determine the setting—time and place—by describing the surroundings and climate.

- Pay attention to every detail, such as the homes in this photograph.

- Find objects in the photograph and determine for what they were used.

- Read the caption, text that describes a picture, for historical context.

Now, review the strategy on the next page to help you analyze this photograph. Then, apply the strategy to the other photographs and paintings in this chapter.

1. Read and Study

★ Pay attention to every detail of the photograph or painting.

★ Consider how the details give clues about the setting, the specific event, and the lifestyle of the people in the photograph or painting.

★ Look for clues about the artist's attitude, or feelings, about the subject of a painting.

★ Read the caption, text that describes a picture. Captions often provide historical context.

2. Ask Yourself Questions

Answer the following questions about the photograph on page 54.

1. Who do you think lived here?

_____

2. What are some reasons that these people may have built their homes into the sides of cliffs?

_____

_____

3. How did these people move from place to place in their village?

_____

_____

4. What does the photograph tell you about the setting?

_____

_____

3. Put It All Together

Draw conclusions about what life might have been like in this village between A.D. 800–1100 based on this photograph.

Practice 1
Analyzing Photographs and Paintings

The Boston Tea Party

Here is a painting about the Boston Tea Party. Read *A Snapshot From History.* It will provide historical background for the painting.

▲ This painting shows the Boston protest of the British Tea Act in 1773.

A Snapshot From History

The French and Indian War had cost the British a great deal of money. Although they won the war, the British were deeply in debt. Feeling that the colonists benefited from the war, the British wanted them to help repay the debts. **Parliament** announced to the colonists that it was imposing new taxes.

In 1773, Parliament issued the Tea Act, which gave a British company a **monopoly** on the tea trade. This meant that colonial tea merchants would be put out of business. Colonists were angry. When three ships brought a new supply of tea into Boston Harbor, the colonists took action. They disguised themselves as Native Americans, boarded the ships, and dumped 342 chests of tea overboard. The Boston Tea Party, as it became known, let the British know that the colonists did not want to be controlled any longer.

Terms To Know ≡

Parliament
the law-making branch of the British government

monopoly
exclusive control

Primary-Source Questions

Use your knowledge of social studies and your American History textbook to help you analyze the painting.

Multiple Choice

Read each item carefully. Circle the number of the correct answer.

1. **Who was involved in the Boston Tea Party?**

   1 Colonists

   2 British soldiers

   3 Parliament

   4 Native Americans

2. **This painting shows colonists**

   1 organizing a demonstration.

   2 preparing to go to war with Great Britain.

   3 tossing chests of tea overboard.

   4 fighting with British soldiers.

3. **Who are the spectators, or onlookers, on shore?**

   1 Native Americans

   2 British Parliament members

   3 British soldiers

   4 Colonists

4. **How do the spectators feel about the Tea Party event?**

   1 They disapprove of the action.

   2 They are cheering in support of the action.

   3 They are angry.

   4 They do not care about what is happening on the ships.

Essay

Write your essay on a separate sheet of paper.

List three details from the painting and tell how they give clues about the setting—time and place—of the event.

Analyzing Photographs and Paintings

The Underground Railroad

Here is a painting about the Underground Railroad. Read
A Snapshot From History. It will provide historical background
for the painting.

▲ This painting shows travelers along the Underground Railroad.

A Snapshot From History

During the mid 1800s, many **abolitionists** found ways to
help enslaved African Americans escape from the South. The
Underground Railroad was one such way. A secret network
of escape routes, the Underground Railroad started in the
South and ran north to Canada and south to Mexico, Cuba,
and the Bahamas. There were a series of stations, or places
where "passengers" could hide along the way. These stations
were houses, churches, and even caves. The escaping African
Americans could get food, clothes, and rest while they journeyed to
freedom. "Conductors" led groups of escapees from one station to
the next.

Term To Know ≣

abolitionist
a person who wanted to
end slavery

Primary-Source Questions

Use your knowledge of social studies and your American History textbook to help you analyze the painting.

Multiple Choice

Read each item carefully. Circle the number of the correct answer.

1. **How are the enslaved African Americans being helped?**

   1 People are giving them jobs in the North.

   2 People are helping them through the snow.

   3 People are giving them food.

   4 People are selling their belongings for money.

2. **Who is helping the enslaved African Americans?**

   1 Slave owners

   2 Enslaved African Americans

   3 White people

   4 Nobody

3. **What can you tell about the escaping African Americans from the painting?**

   1 They are young and vigorous.

   2 There are young, old, weak, and strong people among them.

   3 They are old and weak.

   4 They have never been in the snow before.

4. **Which detail shows that the escaping enslaved African Americans are in danger?**

   1 The dog

   2 The worried looks of the conductors

   3 The harsh weather

   4 The horses pulling the hay wagon

Essay

Write your essay on a separate sheet of paper.

Describe the objects that the escaping African Americans have brought with them. What can you tell about the journey from these details?

Analyzing Photographs and Paintings

Child Labor

Here is a photo from the early 1900s about children who had to work to help their families. Read *A Snapshot From History*. It will provide historical background for the photo.

▲ In the early twentieth century, children in textile factories were paid much less than adults for the same number of hours of work.

A Snapshot From History

By the late 1800s, **industry** in the United States was growing rapidly. Machines and large **factories** changed the way people worked. With machines, products could be made more quickly and efficiently. Work was broken down into separate, simple steps. A different factory worker performed each step, repeating the same task over and over. The need for skilled workers decreased.

By 1910, almost 2 million children worked in factories. Some were as young as six years old. Many children worked 8–12 hours a day in factories, mills, and coal mines. Although some labor laws existed in various states, few laws included protection for children. For this reason, factories hired the cheap labor of young children to tie broken threads or to crawl under machines to oil them. The children in these factories did not go to school and often earned less than a dollar a week.

Terms To Know

industry
large-scale businesses

factories
buildings with workers and machines in which manufacturing takes place

Primary-Source Questions

Use your knowledge of social studies and your American History textbook to help you analyze the photograph.

Constructed Response

Read each question carefully. Write your answer on the lines provided.

1. **Where do the two children in the photograph work?**

   _____

2. **What were working conditions like for these children?**

   _____

   _____

3. **Which details in the photograph show the dangers of the children's job?**

   _____

   _____

   _____

   _____

4. **Based on the details of the photograph, what conclusions can you draw about these children's lives?**

   _____

   _____

   _____

Essay

Write your essay on a separate sheet of paper.

Describe the lives of factory workers in the early twentieth century. Use details in the photograph to support your response.

Americans Raising the Flag

Here are photographs that show the raising of the American flag on two memorable occasions. Read *A Snapshot From History*. It will provide historical background for the photos.

▲ U.S. Marines raise an American flag at Iwo Jima on February 23, 1945.

▲ Firefighters raise an American flag over the remains of the World Trade Center in New York City, September 2001.

A Snapshot From History ▪▪▪▪▪▪▪▪▪▪▪▪▪▪▪▪▪▪

During World War II, the **Allies** fought hard to free islands in the Pacific Ocean from Japanese control. Near the end of the war, the Americans attacked the Japanese-held island of Iwo Jima, about 750 miles away from Tokyo, Japan. The U.S. Marines lost about 6,000 men before they destroyed the strong Japanese **fortifications**. Finally, on February 23, 1945, the Marines climbed Mount Suribachi and planted the American flag. The battle lasted more than a month.

In a terrorist attack on September 11, 2001, hijackers flew two passenger airplanes into the World Trade Center in New York City and another one into the Pentagon in Washington, D.C. A fourth plane crashed in Pennsylvania, after passengers fought with the hijackers. Thousands of innocent people, including many firefighters, police officers, and rescue workers, lost their lives during these terrorist attacks.

Terms To Know ☰

Allies
union of countries, including the United States, who fought the Axis Powers in World War II

fortifications
walls and forts built to defend a place

Primary-Source Questions

Use your knowledge of social studies and your American History textbook to help you analyze the photographs.

Constructed Response

Read each question carefully. Write your answer on the lines provided.

1. **Who are the people depicted in each photograph?**

   _____

   _____

2. **How are these two photographs similar?**

   _____

   _____

   _____

3. **What clues in the photo reveal the setting of the Iwo Jima photo?**

   _____

   _____

   _____

4. **What details reveal the conditions in the World Trade Center photo?**

   _____

   _____

   _____

Essay

Write your essay on a separate sheet of paper.

Compare and contrast the two photographs. Tell what the American flag symbolizes in each photo.

Hands-On Activity

Gather five to seven photos of yourself, your friends, and your family. Create a photo essay of your life by mounting the pictures onto paper and making a cover for your album. Under each picture, write a short caption that tells who the people are, what they are doing, and how they are feeling during that moment in time. Share your photo essay with your class.

CHAPTER 6

Informational Graphics

Model Lesson: Map of the Thirteen Colonies

 Here's the Skill

Informational graphics are visuals, such as maps, charts, graphs, and timelines, that give you facts at a glance. Each type of graphic has its own purpose.

There are many types of maps. For example, a street map can help you get somewhere you've never been before. Other maps may provide information about the geographical features, the political boundaries, or the history of a specific place. The different parts of a map, such as the map key, compass rose, and scale help you to analyze colors, symbols, distances, and direction on a map.

Diagrams, charts, and graphs organize data in different ways and for different purposes. For example, a Venn diagram can be used to compare and contrast two people, places, or events in history. Charts organize categories of information into rows and columns. Not surprisingly, a pie graph looks just like pie. This type of graph helps you to see how different parts of an issue or event fit together to create the whole picture.

Finally, timelines show a sequence of events in the order in which they happened. Specific dates are often provided, as well.

Here's Why

Being able to read informational graphics can help you to see a lot of information in a visual form. A map can help you find your way to a friend's house. If you want to show how many students voted for each candidate in the last student government election, a pie graph can help you. Timelines let you see a sequence of events over a specific period of time. Knowing how to interpret these graphics will help you to be a well-informed citizen.

Read *A Snapshot From History*. It will provide historical background for the map on page 66.

A Snapshot From History

The thirteen colonies differed in geography, climate, and natural resources. As a result, different ways of life slowly emerged throughout the New England, Middle, and Southern colonies.

The New England colonies had long, cold winters and stormy weather conditions. The hard, rocky soil made farming difficult. However, New England had abundant forests and access to the Atlantic Ocean. Thus, many colonists turned to shipbuilding, trading, and fishing.

The moderate climate, abundant resources, and rich, fertile land of the Middle colonies made them a popular place for Europeans to settle. Most people in the Middle colonies made their living by farming.

The Southern colonies had long, warm growing seasons that made farming easy and profitable. Cotton, tobacco, rice, and **indigo** were grown on plantations. Large plantations and smaller farms were widely scattered in the Southern colonies. This made life more isolated than in the other two colonial regions.

Term To Know

indigo
a plant grown and harvested to make a deep blue dye

Here's How ⟱

Look at the following map of the thirteen colonies. The parts of a map are labeled.

The Thirteen Colonies, 1750

0   200   400 miles
0   200   400 kilometers

St. Lawrence R.
45°N
New Hampshire
L. Huron
L. Ontario
New York
L. Erie
Massachusetts
Rhode Island   40°N
Connecticut
Pennsylvania
New Jersey
Ohio R.
Delaware
Maryland
ATLANTIC OCEAN
Virginia
35°N
APPALACHIAN MOUNTAINS
North Carolina
N
W — E
S
South Carolina
Georgia
30°N
Spanish Territory

New England colonies
Middle colonies
Southern colonies
Present-day boundaries

85°W   80°W   75°W

- Read the title to determine the subject, purpose, and date.

- Look at the map scale to see how distances on the map relate to real distances.

- Read all the text and labels. They indicate specific places on the map.

- Check the compass rose. It shows direction—north, south, east, and west.

- Look at the locator map to see the place in relation to a larger area.

- Read the map key to identify what the symbols and colors stand for.

Now, review the step-by-step strategy on the next page to help you analyze this map. Then, apply the strategy to the other informational graphics in this chapter.

66

1. Read and Study

★ Identify the type of the graphic shown.

★ Read the title to determine the subject, purpose, and date of the graphic.

★ Read all the text in the graphic.

★ Pay attention to every detail such as symbols, keys, labels, and colors used. Use these details to interpret the data, or information, provided.

★ Write any words you do not know. Then, check them in a dictionary.

2. Ask Yourself Questions

Answer the following questions about the map on page 66.

1. **What is the subject, purpose, and date of the map?**

   _____

   _____

2. **Which colonies made up the Southern colonies?**

   _____

3. **Which colony was farthest north?**

   _____

4. **Were the Appalachian Mountains east or west of the Southern colonies?**

   _____

5. **Is the state of Georgia larger, or smaller, today than when it was a colony?**

   _____

   _____

3. Put It All Together

Compare and contrast the colonies to the United States today. Use a current map of the United States to help you with your answer.

Venn Diagram of the Federal System

Here is a Venn diagram about the federal system of government. Read *A Snapshot From History*. It will provide historical background for the diagram.

The Federal System

POWERS OF THE NATIONAL GOVERNMENT

- Declare war
- Maintain armed forces
- Establish post offices
- Coin money
- Grant patents and copyrights
- Regulate foreign and interstate trade
- Establish foreign policy
- Set standard weights and measures
- Govern territories and admit states
- Regulate immigration

SHARED POWERS

- Collect taxes
- Borrow money
- Make and enforce laws
- Establish and maintain courts
- Regulate banks
- Provide for public welfare

POWERS OF THE STATE GOVERNMENT

- Maintain schools
- Regulate trade within the state
- Establish local governments
- Set business laws
- Make marriage and divorce laws
- Conduct elections
- Ratify Constitutional amendments

▲ This type of graphic is called a Venn diagram. The powers in the center are shared by both national and state governments.

A Snapshot From History ▪▪▪▪▪▪▪▪▪▪▪▪▪▪▪▪▪▪▪

In the summer of 1787, a group of **delegates** came together for the Constitutional Convention. They struggled to create the Constitution of the United States, a written set of laws that would govern the nation. They made many **compromises**. Some people felt that a stronger national government was needed. Others did not want power taken away from the states and given to the national government.

The Constitution created a **federal** system of government. This system of government divides powers between the national and state governments. It also determines which powers are shared by the national and state governments.

Terms To Know ≣

delegates
representatives sent by individual colonies

compromises
agreements in which both sides give and take to reach a final settlement

federal
national

Primary-Source Questions

Use your knowledge of social studies and your American History textbook to help you analyze the Venn diagram.

Constructed Response

Read each question carefully. Write your answer on the lines provided.

1. **What is the federal system?**

   _____

   _____

2. **Which powers do the state and national governments share?**

   _____

   _____

3. **Which government regulates foreign and interstate trade?**

   _____

   _____

4. **In general, what are the differences between the national and state powers?**

   _____

   _____

   _____

   _____

Essay

Write your essay on a separate sheet of paper.

Why do you think that the Constitution assigned one set of powers to the national government and a different set of powers to the state governments?

Pie Graphs of Women in the Workplace

Here are two pie graphs about women's employment in 1910 and 1930. Read *A Snapshot From History.* It will provide historical background for the pie graphs.

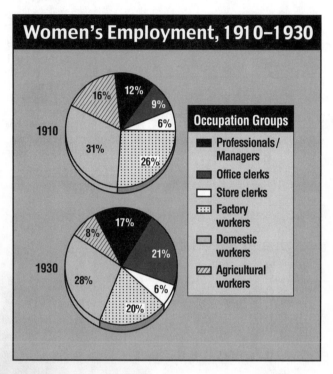

▲ The pie graphs show how the types of jobs held by women changed between 1910 and 1930.

A Snapshot From History

During World War I, many women entered the workforce for the first time. More factory jobs became available because men left these jobs to fight in the war. About 1.5 million women worked in factories to make military supplies.

When the war ended in 1918, nearly all of these women gave up their jobs to **veterans** returning from the war. However, many women liked the independence they had gained by working outside the home. In the 1920s, women began to question their place in **society**. They began to pursue greater intellectual and economic independence by going to college and working in offices.

Terms To Know

veteran
a person who served in the armed forces

society
a group of people in a community

Primary-Source Questions

Use your knowledge of social studies and your American History textbook to help you analyze the pie graphs.

Constructed Response

Read each question carefully. Write your answer on the lines provided.

1. **What percentage of women held jobs in domestic labor in 1910?**

   _____

2. **Which occupation groups had the largest decrease from 1910 to 1930? Why do you think there was a decrease?**

   _____

   _____

   _____

3. **Which occupation stayed the same?**

   _____

4. **Which occupation increased by 5 percent between 1910 and 1930? Why do you think there was an increase?**

   _____

   _____

5. **What impact did World War I have on women's lives?**

   _____

   _____

   _____

Essay

Write your essay on a separate sheet of paper.

In 1930, which kinds of jobs employed a greater percentage of women and which kinds of jobs employed a smaller percentage? What conclusions can you draw from this data?

Chart of State Populations

Here is a chart that lists the ten most populated states in the United States. Read *A Snapshot From History*. It will provide historical background for the chart.

The Ten Most Populated States				
State (U.S.Government Abbreviation)	Total Area in Square Miles (Rank of 50)	Population 2000 Census	Capital	Number of Representatives in House
California (CA)	163,695 (3)	33,871,648	Sacramento	53
Florida (FL)	65,754 (22)	15,982,378	Tallahassee	25
Georgia (GA)	59,424 (24)	8,186,453	Atlanta	13
Illinois (IL)	57,914 (25)	12,419,293	Springfield	19
Michigan (MI)	96,716 (11)	9,938,444	Lansing	15
New Jersey (NJ)	8,721 (47)	8,414,350	Trenton	13
New York (NY)	54,556 (27)	18,976,457	Albany	29
Ohio (OH)	44,824 (34)	11,353,140	Columbus	18
Pennsylvania (PA)	46,055 (33)	12,281,054	Harrisburg	19
Texas (TX)	268,580 (2)	20,851,820	Austin	32

▲ The chart provides data on the ten most populated states in the United States.

A Snapshot From History ■■■■■■■■■■■■■■■■■

Millions of people live in the United States today. Every ten years, the U.S. Bureau of the Census takes an official count of the American people. A population **census** determines the size of a country's population. It also tells various characteristics of its people, such as their age, gender, marital status, ethnic background, occupation, and income. The first census was taken in 1790 and showed that the total population was 3,929,214. In 2000, the census showed that the total U.S. population was 281,421,906.

The national government uses the census data to determine the number of seats each state should have in the House of Representatives. Governments at the city and state levels can also use census data to determine funding for schools or libraries or to decide where to build new roads and bridges.

Term To Know ≣

census
official population count by a national government

Primary-Source Questions

Use your knowledge of social studies and your American History textbook to help you analyze the chart.

Multiple Choice

Read each item carefully. Circle the number of the correct answer.

1. **According to the 2000 census, which state has the most people?**

   1 Georgia

   2 Texas

   3 Michigan

   4 California

2. **Look at Ohio, New York, New Jersey, and Florida. Which of these states has the most representatives in the House?**

   1 Ohio

   2 New York

   3 New Jersey

   4 Florida

3. **Which two states have the highest population and the largest area in square miles?**

   1 Texas and Florida

   2 California and Michigan

   3 Texas and California

   4 Florida and California

4. **In what region of the country are the largest number of highly populated states located?**

   1 East coast

   2 West coast

   3 Midwest

   4 northern Midwest

Essay

Write your essay on a separate sheet of paper.

Based on the data from the chart, determine which state has the most people per square mile and which state has the least. What conclusions can you draw about the lifestyles of the people in each of these states?

A Timeline of Events: Attack on America

Here is a timeline relating to the terrorist attacks against the United States on September 11, 2001. Read *A Snapshot From History*. It will provide historical background for the timeline.

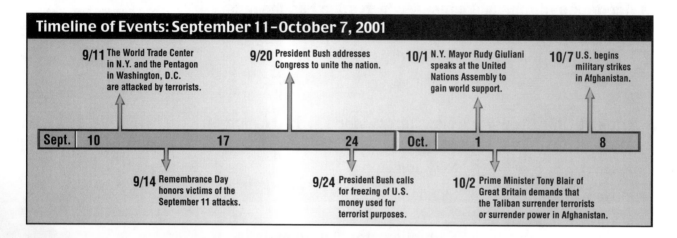

Timeline of Events: September 11–October 7, 2001

9/11 The World Trade Center in N.Y. and the Pentagon in Washington, D.C. are attacked by terrorists.

9/20 President Bush addresses Congress to unite the nation.

10/1 N.Y. Mayor Rudy Giuliani speaks at the United Nations Assembly to gain world support.

10/7 U.S. begins military strikes in Afghanistan.

| Sept. | 10 | 17 | 24 | Oct. | 1 | 8 |

9/14 Remembrance Day honors victims of the September 11 attacks.

9/24 President Bush calls for freezing of U.S. money used for terrorist purposes.

10/2 Prime Minister Tony Blair of Great Britain demands that the Taliban surrender terrorists or surrender power in Afghanistan.

A Snapshot From History ■■■■■■■■■■■■■■■

On September 11, 2001, terrorists attacked the World Trade Center in New York City and the **Pentagon** in Washington, D.C., killing thousands of innocent people. Many Americans were left feeling shocked, sad, angry, and afraid. Countries around the world vowed to join forces with the United States in the fight against **terrorism**.

After the attacks, President George W. Bush addressed Congress and the nation, telling Americans that these "despicable acts of terror . . . cannot touch the **foundation** of America."

The United States began the war on terrorism abroad in the country of Afghanistan, in Central Asia. There, the Taliban government protected Osama bin Laden, the prime suspect in the terrorist attacks. From his hiding places in Afghanistan, bin Laden ran a worldwide network of terrorists called al Qaeda.

The United States wanted the Taliban to hand over bin Laden, but the Taliban refused. As a result, the United States began Operation Enduring Freedom by bombing targets in Afghanistan on October 7, 2001. By the end of 2001, the Taliban and al Qaeda had been driven from power.

Terms To Know ≡

Pentagon
the five-sided building, near Washington D.C., that houses the U.S. Department of Defense

terrorism
using violence or threats to achieve a goal

foundation
the base on which something rests

Primary-Source Questions

Use your knowledge of social studies and your American History textbook to help you analyze the timeline.

Multiple Choice

Read each item carefully. Circle the number of the correct answer.

1. **Which of the following events occurred before President Bush addressed Congress?**

   1 Remembrance Day honors victims.

   2 N.Y. Mayor Guiliani speaks at the United Nations.

   3 U.S. begins to strike Afghanistan.

   4 U.S. freezes money for terrorism.

2. **How many days after the attack did President Bush address Congress?**

   1 4 days

   2 9 days

   3 14 days

   4 17 days

3. **Which event shows that the United States was supported by the international community?**

   1 N.Y. Mayor Guiliani speaks at the United Nations.

   2 U.S. begins to strike Afghanistan.

   3 Remembrance Day honors victims.

   4 Tony Blair of Great Britain demands the Taliban surrender.

4. **When did the U.S. begin military strikes in Afghanistan?**

   1 After Tony Blair demanded Taliban surrender

   2 Before Remembrance Day

   3 After the Taliban surrendered to the United States

   4 Before September 11, 2001

Essay

Write your essay on a separate sheet of paper.

What evidence from the timeline shows how the U.S. and world leaders worked together to combat terrorism?

Hands-On Activity

Choose a current event or issue that interests you. Then, draw a map, chart, graph, or timeline that includes information about your topic. Be sure to include a title that identifies the subject, purpose, and date(s). Share your work with the class, explaining how the graphic helps present information about your topic.

Test 1
Document-Based Question

The Civil War

This test is based on the documents on pages 77–81. As you analyze the documents, take into account both the context and the point of view of each source.

Read *A Snapshot From History*. It will provide historical background for the documents.

A Snapshot From History ■■■■■■■■■■■■■■■■■■

Many Americans believed that the Civil War wouldn't last very long because the North, or the Union, had many advantages over the South, or the Confederacy. For example, the North had a larger population. That meant more men could be called on to fight. Also, the North had many factories that supplied weapons, ammunition, uniforms, and shoes to the soldiers.

President Lincoln wrote the **Emancipation** Proclamation in 1862. It said that on January 1, 1863, all slaves in areas rebelling against the Union would be "forever free." It also said that African Americans could serve in the Union army. These statements led to the **enlistment** of more than 100,000 former slaves in the Union army.

Over the next two years, the northern advantages began to take their toll on the South. Battles such as the one at Gettysburg, Pennsylvania, left the South damaged and weakened. On April 9, 1865, the Confederacy surrendered to the Union army. The war had lasted for four years. More than 600,000 people died, and more than 500,000 were wounded. The cost of the Civil War was huge for both the North and the South.

Terms To Know ≡

emancipation
freedom from slavery

enlistment
voluntary enrollment in the armed forces

Task

Using information from the following documents and your knowledge of social studies, answer the questions that follow each document in Part A. Your answers to the questions will help you write the essay in Part B in which you will be asked to:

★ Discuss the disadvantages the South faced during the war.

★ Discuss the advantages the North had over the South during the war.

★ Discuss how the Emancipation Proclamation contributed to a Union victory.

PART A: SHORT ANSWER

Directions

Analyze the documents, and answer the questions that follow each document in the space provided. Your answers to these questions will help you write the essay on page 82.

Document 1

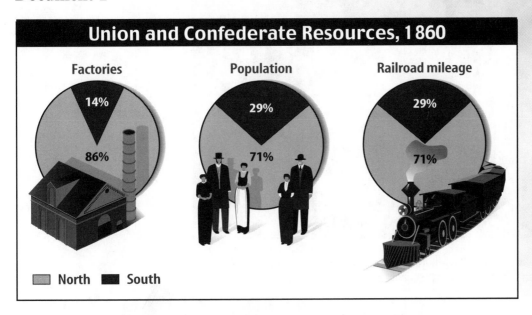

Union and Confederate Resources, 1860

Factories — North 86%, South 14%

Population — North 71%, South 29%

Railroad mileage — North 71%, South 29%

North / South

1. **Based on these pie graphs, list three advantages the North had over the South. Explain why each was an advantage during the Civil War.**

   a. _____

   _____

   _____

   b. _____

   _____

   _____

   c. _____

   _____

   _____

Document 2

▲ The Battle of Gettysburg was fought in Gettysburg, Pennsylvania, in July 1863. It was the deadliest battle and a turning point in the Civil War.

2. **Based on the painting, which army seems to have the advantage? What evidence in the painting supports your response?**

_____

_____

_____

_____

_____

_____

Document 3

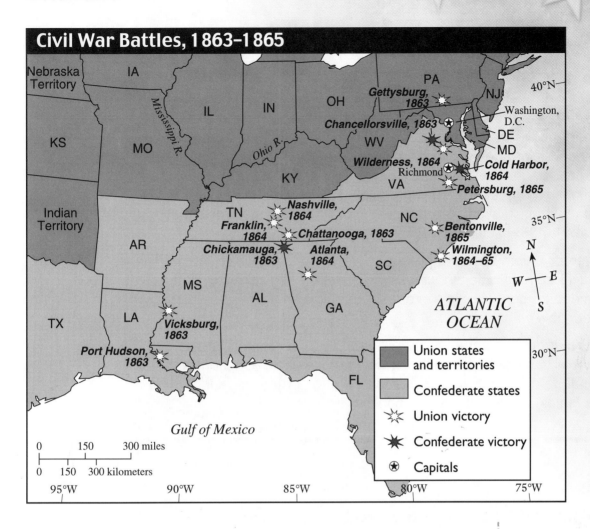

Civil War Battles, 1863–1865

3. **According to this map, where were most of the battles fought—on Confederate land or Union land?**

_____

4. **Which side had more victories?**

_____

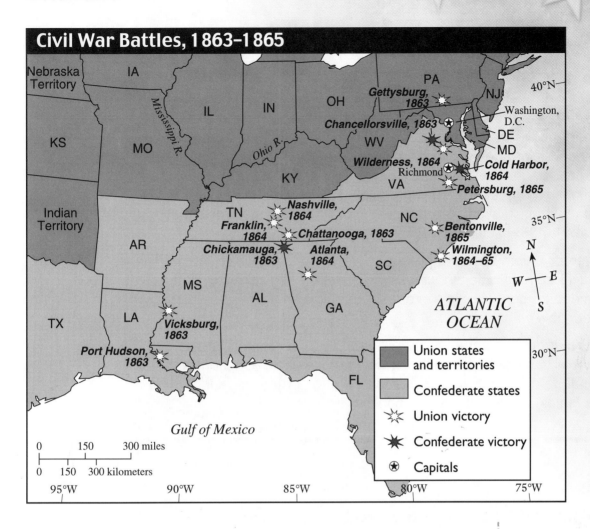

Document 4

From Abraham Lincoln, Emancipation Proclamation (1862)

That on the 1st day of January, A.D. 1863, all persons held as slaves within any State or designated part of a State the people whereof shall then be in rebellion against the United States shall be then, thenceforward, and forever free; and that the executive government of the United States, including the military and naval authority thereof, will recognize and maintain the freedom of such persons, and will do no act or acts to repress [hold back] such persons, or any of them, in any efforts they may make for their actual freedom.

And I hereby enjoin upon the people so declared to be free to abstain [hold back] from all violence, unless in necessary self-defence; and I recommend to them that, in all cases when allowed, they labor faithfully for reasonable wages.

And I further declare and make known that such persons of suitable condition will be received into the armed service of the United States to garrison [guard] forts, positions, stations, and other places, and to man vessels [ships] of all sorts in said service. . . .

5. **What rights did the Emancipation Proclamation give to enslaved African Americans?**

_____

_____

_____

_____

_____

Document 5

From Frederick Douglass, former enslaved African American (1862)

Let the black man get upon his person the brass letters U.S. Let him get an eagle on his button and a musket on his shoulder and bullets in his pocket, and there is no power on earth which can deny that he has earned the right to citizenship in the United States.

6. **According to this document, why should African Americans serve in the Union army?**

   _____

   _____

7. **Why do you think having African American soldiers was an advantage for the Union?**

   _____

   _____

PART B: ESSAY

Directions

★ Write a well-organized essay that includes an introduction, several paragraphs, and a conclusion.

★ Use evidence from the documents to support your response.

★ Include specific, related outside information.

★ Use the three-column chart below to help plan your essay.

Essay

Using your answers and notes from Part A, write your essay on a separate sheet of paper on the following topics:

★ Discuss the disadvantages the South faced during the war.

★ Discuss the advantages the North had over the South during the war.

★ Discuss how the Emancipation Proclamation contributed to a Union victory.

Question	Evidence From Documents	Related Outside Information
• Discuss the disadvantages the South faced during the Civil War.		
• Discuss the advantages the North had during the Civil War.		
• Discuss how the Emancipation Proclamation contributed to a Union victory.		

Test 2
Document-Based Question

The Vietnam War

This test is based on the documents on pages 84–88. As you analyze the documents, take into account both the context and the point of view of each source.

Read *A Snapshot From History*. It will provide historical background for the documents.

A Snapshot From History ∎∎∎∎∎∎∎∎∎∎∎∎∎∎∎∎∎∎

In 1954, the country of Vietnam was divided into the North and the South. However, fighting soon began in South Vietnam. South Vietnam wanted to remain non-Communist. North Vietnam fought to take over South Vietnam to form one Communist nation.

The Ho Chi Minh Trail—named after the leader of North Vietnam—ran through neighboring countries. The United States feared that **communism** might spread throughout Southeast Asia and began sending money, supplies, and advisors to South Vietnam. President Lyndon Johnson sent American soldiers to fight there. As the war continued and many American soldiers were killed, the antiwar movement in the United States grew. People held marches, sang antiwar songs, and wrote letters opposing the war to politicians.

> **Terms To Know** ≣
>
> **communism**
> a one-party government in which the state owns all property

In 1973, President Nixon finally withdrew the last of the U.S. troops from the region. The North Vietnamese won the war and Vietnam became a country united under Communist rule. The Vietnam War was the first war that the United States lost. In 1982, the Vietnam Veterans Memorial was built in Washington, D.C., to honor American soldiers who fought in the war.

Task

Using information from the following documents and your knowledge of social studies, answer the questions that follow each document in Part A. Your answers to the questions will help you write the essay in Part B in which you will be asked to:

★ Discuss the reasons the Vietnamese went to war.

★ Discuss the reasons the United States became involved.

★ Discuss how the Vietnam War negatively affected Americans and Vietnamese people alike.

PART A: SHORT ANSWER

Directions

Analyze the documents, and answer the questions that follow each document in the space provided. Your answers to these questions will help you write the essay on page 89.

Document 1

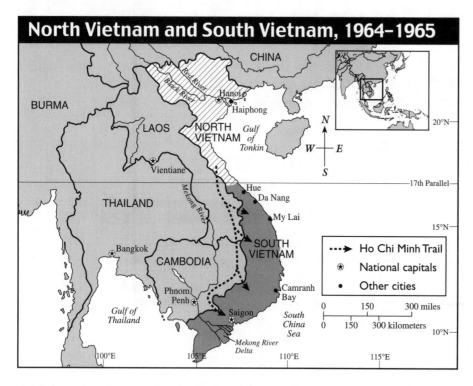

North Vietnam and South Vietnam, 1964–1965

▲ Vietnamese Communists in the North fought against the U.S.-supported South Vietnamese government.

1. **Along what latitude line was Vietnam divided into two separate countries?**

   _____

   _____

2. **How do you think the Vietnam War affected the neighboring countries of Laos and Cambodia?**

   _____

   _____

   _____

Document 2

From President Lyndon Johnson
Speech at Johns Hopkins University (1965)

We are there because we have a promise to keep. Since 1954 every American President has offered support to the people of South Vietnam. We have helped to build, and we have helped to defend. Thus, over many years, we have made a national pledge to help South Vietnam defend its independence. And I intend to keep that promise. . . .

We are also there to strengthen world order. Around the globe, from Berlin to Thailand, are people whose well being rests, in part, on the belief that they can count on us if they are attacked. To leave Vietnam to its fate would shake the confidence of all these people in the value of an American commitment and in the value of America's word. The result would be increased unrest and instability, and even wider war.

Our objective is the independence of South Vietnam, and its freedom from attack. We want nothing for ourselves only that the people of South Vietnam be allowed to guide their own country in their own way. We will do everything necessary to reach that objective. . . .

3. **What reasons did President Johnson give for U.S. involvement in Vietnam?**

_____

_____

_____

_____

_____

_____

Document 3

▲ Both violent and peaceful demonstrations against the Vietnam War took place around the nation.

4. **How does the photograph show the different opinions among Americans about the war?**

_____

_____

_____

Document 4

▲ Many Vietnamese citizens were killed during the war.

5. **What does this political cartoon tell you about what life was like for many Vietnamese people during the war?**

_____

_____

_____

_____

Document 5

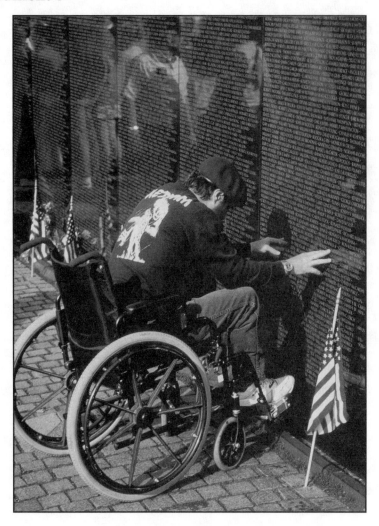

▲ Erected in 1982, the Vietnam Veterans Memorial honors American soldiers of the Vietnam War.

6. Why was the Vietnam Veterans Memorial constructed?

_____

_____

7. According to the photograph, what does the Vietnam Veterans Memorial mean to veterans and their friends and families?

_____

_____

_____

PART B: ESSAY

Directions

★ Write a well-organized essay that includes an introduction, several paragraphs, and a conclusion.

★ Use evidence from the documents to support your response.

★ Include specific, related outside information.

★ Use the Venn diagram below to help you organize your essay.

Essay

Using your answers and notes from Part A, write your essay on a separate sheet of paper on the following topics:

★ Discuss the reasons the Vietnamese went to war.

★ Discuss the reasons the United States became involved.

★ Discuss how the Vietnam War negatively affected Americans and Vietnamese people alike.

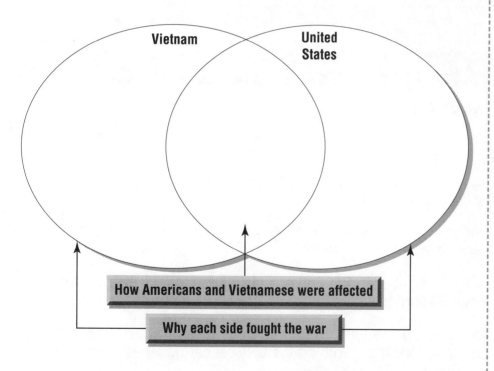

Vietnam   **United States**

How Americans and Vietnamese were affected

Why each side fought the war

Chapter 1 Project: *History Quiz Show*

Who's the Wiz?

Your Task

Using the historical documents from Chapter 1, develop an entertaining quiz show to test your classmates' knowledge of American history.

Step 1: Working with a small team of classmates, re-read the documents. Take notes about each document.

Step 2: Choose questions that can be answered in a word or a phrase. Record each question and answer on the front and back of an index card.

Step 3: Ask volunteers outside of your team to serve as contestants.

Step 4: Conduct your quiz show to determine *Who's the Wiz!*

Chapter 2 Project: *Political Cartoon Contest*

What's the Point?

Your Task

Choose a topic in the news, and draw a political cartoon that reflects your point of view about the issue.

Step 1: Choose a topic that interests you from an article in a daily news-paper, a weekly news magazine, or on the Internet.

Step 2: Draw a political cartoon that reflects your point of view about the topic. Be sure to include any important text and a caption.

Step 3: As a class, display all of your cartoons. Take turns analyzing each cartoon. Then, vote on the political cartoon that is the most informative and interesting.

A Media Frenzy for McKenzie!

Your Task

Develop a media campaign to promote McKenzie, a fictitious candidate, for President. Use advertisements to promote McKenzie.

Step 1: Working in teams, brainstorm a list of qualities that a President should have to run the country effectively.

Step 2: As a team, create a poster to advertise McKenzie's qualities.

Step 3: As a class, display the different posters for McKenzie. Vote on the one that you think will be the most effective tool in the "Media Frenzy for McKenzie!"

You Heard It From the Source

Your Task

Write a firsthand account about a particular event in American history, such as the American Revolution. Then, share your account with viewers across the United States on your show called *You Heard It From the Source!*

Step 1: Working with your team, choose a time in American history about which you enjoyed reading. Brainstorm an important list of people, events, and facts about this period.

Step 2: Choose one kind of firsthand account, such as a letter, autobiography, or oral account. Then, write about the event from the perspective of someone living during this time.

Step 3: As a class, choose one host for the entertainment show. Then, have each team present its account on *You Heard It From the Source.*

A Portrait of America

Your Task

Find photos of a person or an event in contemporary American history. Create a photo essay called "A Portrait of America."

Step 1: Work with your team to find photos in newspapers, magazines, and the Internet about a particular person or an event in the current news. You can even use your camera to take a primary-source photo! Choose the subject from one of the following areas: politics, world news, medicine, entertainment, space exploration, business, transportation, education, or communication.

Step 2: Mount your photos onto posterboard. Work with your team members to write captions that describe each photo and that work together to tell a story.

Step 3: Share your photo essay with the rest of the class. Then, create a place in the classroom to display the photo essays. Above the area, create a sign that says, "A Portrait of America."

The Mapping of America

Your Task

Create maps and an accompanying timeline that illustrate what happened in America in the past.

Step 1: Have each team choose a different period of American history.

Step 2: Use a library and the Internet to gather information to create a map.

Step 3: Have team members work on different parts of the map such as the outline, color, important features, labels, and so on.

Step 4: Then as a class, create a timeline that shows the historical sequence of the events pictured in the maps. Display the timeline on a large posterboard in the classroom. Hang the maps in chronological order along the timeline.

A

abolitionist a person who wanted to end slavery (p. 58)

acid rain rain containing acids formed by pollutants from burning fossil fuels (p. 26)

adobe sun-dried bricks made of clay and straw (p. 53)

Allies union of countries, including the United States, who fought the Axis Powers in World War II (p. 62)

amendment a change to a document (p. 8)

archaeological evidence signs used in the study of past life and cultures (p. 53)

B

battlefield an area in which an armed combat is fought (p. 46)

Bill of Rights the first ten amendments to the U.S. Constitution (p. 8)

boycott a protest in which people refuse to buy products or use services (p. 24)

C

census official population count by a national government (p. 72)

Civil War a war between people of the same country (p. 12)

cliff dwelling a home built into the side of a cliff (p. 53)

colony a settlement in a distant land that is governed by another country (p. 32)

communism a one-party government in which the state owns all property (p. 83)

compact a formal agreement (p. 10)

compromise an agreement in which both sides give and take to reach a final settlement (p. 68)

Confederate southern (p. 12)

convention an official gathering (p. 8)

D

delegate a representative sent by an individual colony (p. 68)

depression a long period of economic problems (p. 22)

desegregation the abolishment of racial separation, especially in public schools (p. 50)

drafted required to serve in a nation's armed forces for a specific period (p. 41)

E

emancipation freedom from slavery (p. 76)

enlistment voluntary enrollment in the armed forces (p. 76)

Environmental Protection Agency government-run organization that works to protect the environment (p. 26)

F

factory a building with workers and machines in which manufacturing takes place (p. 60)

federal national (p. 68)

First Lady wife of the President, a governor, or a mayor (p. 44)

fortification a wall or fort built to defend a place (p. 62)

foundation the base on which something rests (p. 74)

I

inaugural address a speech that an elected official gives when inducted or admitted into office (p. 14)

indigo a plant grown and harvested to make a deep blue dye (p. 65)

industry large-scale businesses (p. 60)

internment camp a place in which people are confined, especially during a time of war (p. 48)

M

moderate having mild, reasonable opinions (p. 34)

monopoly exclusive control (p. 56)

P

Parliament the law-making branch of the British government (p. 56)

Pentagon the five-sided building near Washington, D.C., that houses the U.S. Department of Defense (p. 74)

Pilgrim a person who travels to a new land (p. 10)

plantation a large farm requiring many workers (p. 32)

prairie the flat, rolling land of the Great Plains (p. 29)

presidential nomination the naming of a person by a political party to be a candidate in a presidential election (p. 34)

protest meeting to express disapproval (p. 5)

Puritan a member of religious group that wanted to simplify the practices of the Church of England (p. 10)

R

Reconstruction the period from 1865–1877, in which programs were created to reunite the South with the North (p. 20)

republic a government that takes its power from the people, who elect its leaders (p. 8)

S

segregated racially separated (p. 50)

segregation separation of the races (p. 24)

sit-in a protest in which people refuse to leave a place (p. 24)

society a group of people in a community (p. 70)

squadron a unit of air force fighter pilots (p. 41)

Supreme Court the highest court in the United States (p. 17)

T

terrorism using violence or threats to achieve a goal (p. 74)

transcontinental across a continent (p. 29)

U

Union northern (p. 12)

V

veteran a person who served in the armed forces (p. 70)

W

workforce total number of people employed in a nation (p. 38)

INDEX

Index Key: *ad* = advertisement; *c* = cartoon; *crt* = chart or graph; *m* = map; *p* = painting or photograph; *t* = timeline